THIS
JOURNAL
BELONGS TO

_____

_"Practice the presence of peace.
The more you do that, the more
you will feel the presence of
that power in your life."_
—_Paramahansa Yogananda_

✻ J O U R N A L ✻

I N N E R
P E A C E

WITH INSPIRATIONAL THOUGHTS FROM

PARAMAHANSA YOGANANDA

Self-Realization Fellowship
FOUNDED 1920
Paramahansa Yogananda

Authorized by the International Publications Council of
SELF-REALIZATION FELLOWSHIP
3880 San Rafael Avenue
Los Angeles, California 90065-3298

The Self-Realization Fellowship name and emblem (shown above) appear on all SRF books, recordings, and other publications, assuring the reader that a work originates with the society established by Paramahansa Yogananda and faithfully conveys his teachings.

Designed by Nita Ybarra

ISBN 0-87612-011-7
Printed in the United States of America
13134-54321

INTRODUCTION

"You have made yourself what you are now, and you can become whatever you want to be."

—Paramahansa Yogananda

As you fill the pages of this journal, may it become for you a companion for daily reflection and self-unfoldment. Within the human spirit is an image of Divinity—a potential for nobility, creative initiative, and infinite joy. By delving into the inner self, and writing down the thoughts and aspirations discovered there, we come to recognize and identify with the deeper aspects of our being, with all its sublime soul-qualities.

To become a peaceful being, it is necessary to not merely read about spiritual truths, but to apply them. The quotations in this journal have been chosen with that in mind. They have been drawn from the words of Paramahansa Yogananda to inspire your inner reflections, motivate your behavior, and help you to gauge your progress toward a more balanced, peaceful existence. On various pages you will find action-oriented suggestions for goals to achieve and obstacles to overcome, as well as concise gems of wisdom to stimulate your introspection. Dwell on these prior to writing in your journal; take a few moments to visualize and feel the spiritual perceptions behind the words, and then write about how they apply to your own life—this practice can be a powerful aid to integrating God's peace and guidance into your actions, attitudes, and relationships.

The contents of *Inner Peace Journal* are primarily from the companion volume, *Inner Peace: How to Be Calmly Active and Actively Calm,* with additional counsel from Paramahansa Yogananda on the value of daily introspection for self-improvement. "It is a good idea to keep a mental diary," he said. "Before you go to bed each night, sit for a short time and review the day. See what you are becoming. Do you like the trend of your life? If not, change it." The use of this journal will help you to live from a center of calmness and peace, from which you will be able to make those positive changes that will enrich your life in every way.

— Self-Realization Fellowship

LIVE EACH PRESENT
MOMENT COM-
PLETELY AND THE
FUTURE WILL TAKE
CARE OF ITSELF.
FULLY ENJOY THE
WONDER AND
BEAUTY OF EACH
INSTANT.

what makes me sad
- the world 💔
- self
- social awkwardness (in articulate)
- low self-value / worth
- my upbringing
- inheritance of depression (biology)
- thinking that nobody really
likes me (I'm somewhat unlikeable)
- forever feeling like I'm not
like many other people
- focus / concentration (lack of)
- crabby / cranky
- wasting time being depressed -
not doing things I really want
to be doing

* Hank's illness

all becoming overwhelming - not good
at handling it all at once.

People I love

Gn
Hank
Rachel
Nina
Ned
Karen
Cliff
Tanya   Anna & Linda
Owen W.   Chickie & Artie
Martha K.   Marlene's mom
                         Marlene B.
Laura G   Phranque
Lara   Bruce Wild
Rod + Sandra   Chris Gum
A.I. + cousins + fams   Jeff H.
Fiore cousins   Sue B.
Jesse F.   Jesse G.   fam in Bagni
Sarah K.   Bonnie Oskin

FORGET THE PAST, FOR IT IS GONE FROM YOUR DOMAIN! FORGET THE FUTURE, FOR IT IS BEYOND YOUR REACH! CONTROL THE PRESENT! LIVE SUPREMELY WELL NOW!...THIS IS THE WAY OF THE WISE.

What do you think / hope / expect to be able to do for me?

How much can I hope to heal / relieve my sadness?

What is a realistic expectation for me?

How does a "healthy" person deal / cope with this stuff and how can I get closer to that ability in myself?

What helped last week —
MINDFULNESS — stay in the
moment. If it's good, bad or other—
but try to enjoy the good moments in
the moment. Be outside and appreciate
the springtime, the air, don't get
dragged down by the misery in
life.

Bernie Siegel
Peace love & healing

TURN TO A SINCERE
SEARCH FOR FUL-
FILLMENT IN INNER
CALMNESS, INTRO-
SPECTION, AND DIS-
CRIMINATIVE
ACTION....PERFORM
ALL ACTIONS
GUIDED ONLY BY
WISDOM AND SELF-
CONTROL.

not moving forward —
could have stayed in
bed all week, but didn't,
but otherwise not a lot
accomplished
fitness concerns —
self concerns —
Still need to know how
to rise above it all, to

The Promise of Winter

W RITE DOWN
YOUR THOUGHTS
AND ASPIRATIONS
DAILY. FIND OUT
WHAT YOU ARE—
NOT WHAT YOU
IMAGINE YOU ARE!—
BECAUSE YOU WANT
TO MAKE YOURSELF
WHAT YOU OUGHT
TO BE.

holding back on feeling
grief - afraid of it overwhelming
me?
how to not let grief become
depression -
guilt over not feeling
sad -

Do not sink into the rut of mediocrity. Rise above the crowd. Step out of the choking monotony of ordinary existence into a finer, more colorful life of achievement and ever new peace.

Everything you do should be done with peace. That is the best medicine for your body, mind, and soul. It is the most wonderful way to live.

Look at the perpetual current of emotions and thoughts that arise within you. Go into the heart of your aspirations, dreams, hopes, and despairs. Dive deep into the mute cravings of your inner self....Seek understanding with your highest intelligence, wisdom, love, and vision.

PRACTICE THE PRES-
ENCE OF PEACE. THE
MORE YOU DO THAT,
THE MORE YOU WILL
FEEL THE PRESENCE
OF THAT POWER IN
YOUR LIFE.

PEACE EMANATES
FROM THE SOUL,
AND IS THE SACRED
INNER ENVIRON-
MENT IN WHICH
TRUE HAPPINESS
UNFOLDS.

PLACE YOUR HEART
WITH GOD. THE
MORE YOU SEEK
PEACE IN HIM, THE
MORE THAT PEACE
WILL DEVOUR YOUR
WORRIES AND
SUFFERINGS.

ONE UNITED TO
"THE PEACE OF GOD,
WHICH PASSETH ALL
UNDERSTANDING" IS
LIKE A LOVELY ROSE,
SPREADING AROUND
HIM THE FRAGRANCE
OF TRANQUILITY
AND HARMONY.

IF [ONE] CONQUERS
OTHERS' QUARREL-
SOME DISPOSITIONS
BY HIS CONSTANT,
BEAUTIFUL EXPRES-
SIONS OF UNDYING
LOVE, THEN HE WILL
BECOME A PRINCE
OF PEACE.

Every night, sit still and ask yourself, "What have I done today?" This will help you to see clearly how you can use your time more wisely. If you remember just this one key, you will become a different person.

Man's great
need is to find
more time to
enjoy nature, to
simplify his
life,...to learn to
know his children
and friends bet-
ter, and most of
all, to know *him-
self* and the God
who made him.

FOCUS YOUR
ATTENTION WITHIN.
YOU WILL FEEL A
NEW POWER, A NEW
STRENGTH, A NEW
PEACE—IN BODY,
MIND, AND SPIRIT.

INTROSPECT EVERY
NIGHT...AND NOW
AND THEN DURING
THE DAYTIME BE
STILL FOR A MINUTE,
AND ANALYZE WHAT
YOU ARE DOING
AND THINKING.
THOSE WHO DON'T
ANALYZE THEM–
SELVES NEVER
CHANGE.

EACH DAY HAS A LESSON TO TEACH....TRUE SELF-ANALYSIS IS THE GREATEST ART OF PROGRESS.

IF YOU KEEP YOUR
MIND ON THE
RESOLVE NEVER TO
LOSE YOUR PEACE,
THEN YOU CAN
ATTAIN GODLINESS.

Keep a secret chamber of silence within yourself, where you will not let moods, trials, battles, or inharmony enter. Keep out all hatred, revengefulness, and desires. In this chamber of peace God will visit you.

INTROSPECTION IS
A MIRROR IN WHICH
TO SEE RECESSES OF
YOUR MIND THAT
OTHERWISE WOULD
REMAIN HIDDEN
FROM YOU. ANALYZE
WHAT YOU ARE,
WHAT YOU WISH TO
BECOME, AND WHAT
SHORTCOMINGS ARE
IMPEDING YOU.

When you have peace in every movement of your body, peace in your thinking and in your will power, peace in your love, and peace and God in your ambitions, remember, you have connected your life with God.

⚜

PRACTICE MEDITA-
TION AND GOD-
COMMUNION REGU-
LARLY, AND YOU
WILL TASTE THE
WINE OF JOY AND
PLEASANTNESS ALL
THE TIME, NO
MATTER WHAT
YOUR OUTER
CIRCUMSTANCES.

CALMNESS IS THE LIVING BREATH OF GOD'S IMMORTAL-ITY IN YOU.

THE KINGDOM OF
GOD IS JUST BEHIND
THE DARKNESS OF
CLOSED EYES, AND
THE FIRST GATE
THAT OPENS TO IT IS
YOUR PEACE.

Exhale and relax, and feel peace spread everywhere, within and without. Immerse yourself in that peace.

LIFE IS FULL OF
BUMPS AND
KNOCKS. IN THE
HOURS OF TRIALS,
WHICH DEMAND
YOUR KEENEST
JUDGMENT, IF YOU
PRESERVE YOUR
MENTAL EQUILIB-
RIUM YOU WILL
ATTAIN VICTORY.

THE BEST CURE FOR
NERVOUSNESS IS THE
CULTIVATION OF
CALMNESS. ONE
WHO IS NATURALLY
CALM DOES NOT
LOSE HIS SENSE OF
REASON, JUSTICE, OR
HUMOR UNDER ANY
CIRCUMSTANCES.

WHEN YOU
WORRY, THERE IS
STATIC COMING
THROUGH YOUR
MIND RADIO. GOD'S
SONG IS THE SONG
OF CALMNESS.
NERVOUSNESS IS THE
STATIC; CALMNESS IS
THE VOICE OF GOD
SPEAKING TO YOU
THROUGH THE
RADIO OF YOUR
SOUL.

THROUGH MEDITA-
TION ONE CAN
EXPERIENCE A STA-
BLE, SILENT INNER
PEACE THAT CAN BE
A PERMANENTLY
SOOTHING BACK-
GROUND FOR ALL
HARMONIOUS
OR TRIALSOME
ACTIVITIES.

THE MORE YOU
FEEL PEACE IN MEDI-
TATION, THE CLOSER
YOU ARE TO GOD.
HE MOVES NEARER
AND NEARER TO
YOU THE DEEPER
YOU ENTER INTO
MEDITATION.

LET GO AND
RELAX....WHEN YOU
ARE CALM, YOU FEEL
THE WHOLE UNI-
VERSE OF HAPPINESS
ROCKING GENTLY
BENEATH YOUR
CONSCIOUSNESS.
THAT HAPPINESS IS
GOD.

PEACE IS THE
ENJOYMENT OF LIFE:
ACTIVITY IS THE
EXPRESSION OF LIFE.
A BALANCE
BETWEEN THE
ACTIVITY OF THE
WEST AND THE
CALMNESS OF THE
EAST IS NEEDED.

AFFIRM OFTEN: "I
WILL BE CALMLY
ACTIVE, ACTIVELY
CALM. I AM A
PRINCE OF PEACE,
SITTING ON THE
THRONE OF POISE,
DIRECTING THE
KINGDOM OF MY
ACTIVITY."

PRACTICE THE ART
OF LIVING IN THIS
WORLD WITHOUT
LOSING YOUR INNER
PEACE OF MIND.
FOLLOW THE
PATH OF BALANCE
TO REACH THE
INNER WONDROUS
GARDEN OF SELF-
REALIZATION.

Learn to be very active in this world, doing constructive work; but when you are through with your duties,...retire to the center of your being, which is calmness.

❧❧❧

HARMONIZE YOUR THOUGHTS AND DESIRES WITH THE ALL-FULFILLING REALITIES YOU ALREADY POSSESS IN YOUR SOUL. THEN YOU WILL SEE THE UNDERLYING HAR-MONY IN YOUR LIFE AND IN ALL NATURE.

ISN'T IT BETTER TO LIVE SIMPLY—WITHOUT SO MANY LUXURIES AND WITH FEWER WORRIES? THERE IS NO PLEASURE IN DRIVING YOURSELF UNTIL YOU CANNOT ENJOY WHAT YOU HAVE.

OPEN THE DOOR
OF YOUR CALMNESS
AND LET THE FOOT-
STEPS OF SILENCE
GENTLY ENTER THE
TEMPLE OF ALL
YOUR ACTIVITIES.

PERFORM ALL
DUTIES SERENELY,
SATURATED WITH
PEACE. BEHIND THE
THROB OF YOUR
HEART, YOU SHALL
FEEL THE THROB OF
GOD'S PEACE.

AWAKEN THE
INNATE FORTITUDE
OF THE MIND BY
AFFIRMING, "NO
MATTER WHAT
EXPERIENCES COME,
THEY CANNOT
TOUCH ME. I AM
ALWAYS HAPPY."

THE BEST WAY TO LIVE IS TO TAKE LIFE AS A COSMIC GAME, WITH ITS INEVITABLE CONTRASTS OF DEFEAT AND VICTORY. ENJOY THE CHALLENGES AS YOU WOULD IN A SPORT, NO MATTER WHETHER AT THE MOMENT YOU ARE VICTORIOUS OR VANQUISHED.

This world is but a stage on which you play your parts under the direction of the Divine Stage Manager. Play them well, whether they are tragic or comic, always remember-ing that your real nature is eternal Bliss, and nothing else.

꧁꧂

Once you have
touched the
source of truth
and life, all
nature will
respond to you.
Finding God
within, you will
find Him without,
in all people and
all conditions.

WHEN YOU KNOW
GOD AS PEACE
WITHIN, THEN YOU
WILL REALIZE HIM
AS PEACE EXISTING
IN THE UNIVERSAL
HARMONY OF ALL
THINGS WITHOUT.

ABOUT THE AUTHOR

PARAMAHANSA YOGANANDA (1893–1952) is widely regarded as one of the preeminent spiritual figures of our time. Born in northern India, he came to the United States in 1920, where for more than thirty years he taught India's ancient science of meditation and the art of balanced spiritual living. Through his acclaimed life story, *Autobiography of a Yogi,* and his numerous other books, Paramahansa Yogananda has introduced millions of readers to the perennial wisdom of the East. Under the guidance of one of his earliest and closest disciples, Sri Daya Mata, his spiritual and humanitarian work is carried on by Self-Realization Fellowship, the international society he founded in 1920 to disseminate his teachings worldwide.

OTHER BOOKS BY
PARAMAHANSA YOGANANDA

Available at bookstores or directly from the publisher

Autobiography of a Yogi
Autobiography of a Yogi *(Audiobook, read by Ben Kingsley)*
God Talks With Arjuna: *The Bhagavad Gita (A New Translation and Commentary)*

The Collected Talks and Essays
Volume I: Man's Eternal Quest
Volume II: The Divine Romance
Volume III: Journey to Self-realization: *Discovering the Gifts of the Soul*

Wine of the Mystic: *The Rubaiyat of Omar Khayyam—A Spiritual Interpretation*
The Science of Religion
Whispers from Eternity
Songs of the Soul
Sayings of Paramahansa Yogananda
Scientific Healing Affirmations
Where There Is Light: *Insight and Inspiration for Meeting Life's Challenges*
In the Sanctuary of the Soul: *A Guide to Effective Prayer*
Inner Peace: *How to Be Calmly Active and Actively Calm*
How You Can Talk With God
Metaphysical Meditations
The Law of Success
Cosmic Chants
A World in Transition: Finding Spiritual Security in Times of Change
(Anthology—Paramahansa Yogananda and other monastics
of Self-Realization Fellowship)

Self-Realization Fellowship Lessons

The scientific techniques of meditation taught by Paramahansa Yogananda, including *Kriya Yoga*—as well as his guidance on all aspects of balanced spiritual living—are taught in the Self-Realization Fellowship Lessons. For further information, you are welcome to write for the free booklet, *Undreamed-of Possibilities*.

SELF-REALIZATION FELLOWSHIP
3880 San Rafael Avenue ◆ Los Angeles, CA 90065-3298
tel (323) 225-2471 ◆ fax (323) 225-5088
www.yogananda-srf.org